Bank Financial Group

Ed Clark
President and CEO
TD Bank Financial Group

Dear Readers,

TD would like to present you with this gift to take home, read and enjoy!

Alligator Stew: Favourite Poems by Dennis Lee is a treasury of some of the best-loved poems ever written for Canadian children. In this special collection, you will find lots of reasons to smile and giggle as you read each and every verse.

All of us at TD are excited to give you, and every Grade One student in Canada, a copy of *Alligator Stew*. It's our way of celebrating TD Canadian Children's Book Week, one of several children's reading programs we support each year across the country. We encourage ʸ to visit your local library to discover the magical world of ¹

Have fun reading!

Ed Clark

Ed Clark

TD150

The poems in this book have appeared previously in the following collections: *Alligator Pie* (1974), *Jelly Belly* (1983), *Bubblegum Delicious* (2000) and *Garbage Delight: Another Helping* (2002). This edition was prepared for the Canadian Children's Book Centre by Key Porter Books Limited.

Special edition prepared for the TD Grade One Book Giveaway Program.

Printed in Canada by Friesens Corporation.

Also available in French: Ragoût de crocodile

ISBN 0-929095-25-1 (English) paperback
ISBN 0-929095-27-8 (French) paperback

Library and Archives Canada Cataloguing in Publication

Lee, Dennis, 1959–
    Alligator stew : favourite poems / by Dennis Lee ; illustrated by Rogé. —
Special ed. prepared for the TD Grade One Book Giveaway Program

ISBN 0-929095-25-1

I. Rogé, 1972- II. Title.

PS8523.E3A845 2005   jC811'.54   C2005-903936-1

Key Porter Kids is an imprint of
Key Porter Books Limited
Six Adelaide Street East, Tenth Floor
Toronto, Ontario
Canada M5C 1H6

www.keyporter.com

Text design: Peter Maher

Printed and bound in Canada

The Canadian Children's Book Centre
40 Orchard View Blvd
Suite 101
Toronto, Ontario
Canada M4R 1B9

www.bookcentre.ca

Alligator Stew

Favourite Poems
by Dennis Lee

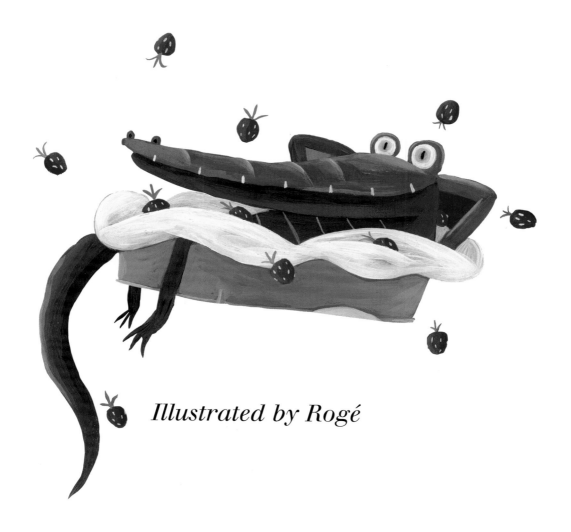

Illustrated by Rogé

KPk
Key Porter Kids

The Canadian Children's Book Centre

Alligator Pie

Alligator pie, alligator pie,
If I don't get some I think I'm gonna die.
Give away the green grass, give away the sky,
But don't give away my alligator pie.

Alligator stew, alligator stew,
If I don't get some I don't know what I'll do.
Give away my furry hat, give away my shoe,
But don't give away my alligator stew.

Alligator soup, alligator soup,
If I don't get some I think I'm gonna droop.
Give away my hockey-stick, give away my hoop,
But don't give away my alligator soup.

Willoughby Wallaby Woo

Willoughby, wallaby, woo.
I don't know what to do.

Willoughby, wallaby, wee.
An elephant sat on me.

Willoughby, wallaby, wash.
I'm feeling kind of squash.

Willoughby, wallaby, woo.
And I don't know what to do.

Goober and Guck

Goober and guck,
Goober and guck,
We're making a sandwich
Of goober and guck.

It won't make you healthy
Or bring you good luck,
But gobble it down and
You'll quack like a duck;

You'll quack like a duck and
You'll smell like a truck—
So eat your nice sandwich
Of goober and guck!

Billy Batter

Billy Batter,
What's the matter?
How come you're so sad?
    I lost my cat
    In the laundromat,
And a dragon ran off with my dad,
    My dad—
A dragon ran off with my dad!

Billy Batter,
What's the matter?
How come you're so glum?
    I ripped my jeans
    On the Coke machine,
And a monster ran off with my mum,
    My mum—
A monster ran off with my mum!

Billy Batter,
    Now you're better—
Happy as a tack!
    The dragon's gone
    To Saskatchewan;
    The monster fell
    In a wishing-well;
    The cat showed up
    With a new-born pup;
    I fixed the rips
    With potato chips,
And my dad and my mum came back,
    Came back—
My dad and my mum came back!

The Muddy Puddle

I am sitting
In the middle
Of a rather Muddy
Puddle,
With my bottom
Full of bubbles
And my rubbers
Full of Mud,

While my jacket
And my sweater
Go on slowly
Getting wetter
As I very
Slowly settle
To the bottom
Of the Mud.

And I find that
What a person
With a puddle
Round his middle
Thinks of mostly
In the muddle
Is the Muddi-
Ness of Mud.

The Swing

The swing swings up,
    And the swing swings down,
And the swing swings wishing-wings
    High over town.

And when it goes high,
    And it starts to sway,
I'll hang for a minute
    Or hang for a day;

And when it goes low,
    And it starts to whizz,
I'll fly through the air
    Till I feel it fizz.

But the swing swings up,
    And the swing swings down,
And the swing swings wishing-wings
    High over town.

Psychapoo

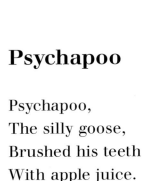

Psychapoo,
The silly goose,
Brushed his teeth
With apple juice.

Psychapoo,
The melon head,
Rode his bicycle
In bed.

His mother said,
"Sit down and eat!"
He swallowed the
plate
And left the meat.

His father asked
him,
"Can't you hear?"
He had a carrot
In his ear.

He met a dog
And shook its tail,
Took a bath
And caught a whale,

Put it in his
Piggy bank,
Said, "I think I'll
Call it Frank."

His brother asked
him,
"Can't you see?"
He drank his hair
And combed his tea.

He took a trip
To Newfoundland,
Walking on water
And swimming on
land

And every time
He heard a shout,
He took his pencil
And rubbed it out.

It isn't me,
It isn't you,
It's nutty, mutty
Psychapoo.

Bubblegum Delicious

Bubblegum delicious,
Bubblegum delight,
Bubblegum de-lovely in the
Middle of the night.

Wrap you up in bubble wrap,
Wrap you up in gum,
Wrap you up in wonderful
'Cause you're the special one!

The Faithful Donut

(Slowly, with feeding)

Far across the ocean,
  Far across the sea,
A faithful jelly donut
  Is waiting just for me.

Its sugar shines with longing,
  Its jelly glows with tears;
My donut has been waiting there
  For twenty-seven years.

O faithful jelly donut,
  I beg you; don't despair!
My teeth are in Toronto, but
  My heart is with you there.

And I will cross the ocean,
  And I will cross the sea,
And I will crush you to my lips;
  And make you one with me.

Skyscraper

Skyscraper, skyscraper,
Scrape me some sky:
Tickle the sun
While the stars go by.

Tickle the stars
While the sun's climbing high,
Then skyscraper, skyscraper,
Scrape me some sky.

Eh, Mon

Eh, mon,
Cool, mon—
You a silly
Fool, mon.

Double-barrelled Ding-dong-bat

Why,
You—

Double-barrelled,
Disconnected,
Supersonic
Ding-dong-bat:

Don't you dare come
Near me, or I'll
Disconnect you
Just like that!

Anna Banana

Anna Banana, jump into the stew:
Gravy and carrots are *good* for you.
    Good for your teeth
    And your fingernails too,
So Anna Banana, jump into the stew!

Tony Baloney

Tony Baloney is fibbing again—
Look at him wiggle and try to pretend.
Tony Baloney is telling a lie:
Phony old Tony Baloney, goodbye!

The Ghost and Jenny Jemima

(slow and spooky)

The clock struck one,
The clock struck two,
The ghost came playing
Peekaboo.
    Wa-OOO!
    Wa-OOO!

The clock struck three,
The clock struck four,
And Jenny Jemima
Began to roar.
    Wa-OOO!
    Wa-OOO!

The clock struck five,
The clock struck six,
The ghost could walk through
Steel and bricks.
    Wa-OOO!
    Wa-OOO!

The clock struck seven,
The clock struck eight,
And Jenny Jemima's
Hair stood straight.
   Wa-OOO!
   Wa-OOO!

The clock struck nine,
The clock struck ten...
The ghost wound the clock,
And went home again.

THE END

Worm

Some people think a worm is rude,
'Cause he's mostly not in a talkative mood.

And other people think he's dumb,
'Cause he likes you to call, but he doesn't come.

But I've got a worm, and his name is Worm,
And he lives in a jar with a bunch of germs,

And Worm is as smart as a worm can be;
I talk to him, and he listens to me.

I tell him the time I fell downstairs
And I teach him the names of my teddy bears

And we both sit still, and I hear the things
That you hear when a worm begins to sing—

About dirt in the yard, and tunnels, and drains,
And having a bath in the grass when it rains.

And we plan about snacks, and not washing your hands,
And the letter J. And he understands.

The Dreadful Doings of Jelly Belly

Jelly Belly bit
    With a big fat bite.
Jelly Belly fought
    With a big fat fight.

Jelly Belly scowled
    With a big fat frown.
Jelly Belly yelled
    Till his house fell down.

In Kamloops

In Kamloops
I'll eat your boots.

In the Gatineaus
I'll eat your toes.

In Napanee
I'll eat your knee.

In Winnipeg
I'll eat your leg.

In Charlottetown
I'll eat your gown.

In Crysler's Farm
I'll eat your arm.

In Aklavik
I'll eat your neck.

In Red Deer
I'll eat your ear.

In Trois Rivières
I'll eat your hair.

In Kitimat
I'll eat your hat.

And I'll eat your nose
And I'll eat your toes
In Medicine Hat and Moose Jaw.

Doctor Bop

The band was playing dixie
The band was playing swing
But Doctor Bop was rocking
With a boogie-woogie thing.

They told him play some dixie
They told him play some swing
But Doctor Bop just wouldn't stop
That boogie-woogie thing—

'Cause he had hot stuff, cool stuff
Good old break-the-rules stuff
Stuff with jelly, stuff with jam
Boogie-woogie stuff with a sis-boom-bam!

Thinking in Bed

I'm thinking in bed,
'Cause I can't get out
Till I learn how to think
What I'm thinking about;
What I'm thinking about
Is a person to be—
A sort of a person
Who feels like me.

I might still be Alice,
Excepting I'm not.
And Snoopy is super,
But not when it's hot;
I couldn't be Piglet,
I don't think I'm Pooh,
I know I'm not Daddy
And I can't be you.

My breakfast is waiting.
My clothes are all out,
But *what* was that thing
I was thinking about?
I'll never get up
If I lie here all day;
But I still haven't thought,
So I'll just have to stay.

If I was a Grinch
I expect I would know.
I might have been Batman,
But I don't think so.
There's so many people
I don't seem to be—
I guess I'll just have to
Get up and be me.

Mulligan Stew

Mulligan stew, mulligan stew,
It's quick and delicious and good for you too.
Shoot it from cannons or use it for glue—
It's mulligan, mulligan, mulligan stew.

Mulligan stew, mulligan stew,
Cheap at the price and it won't make you spew.
It sets like cement, it grows hair on a shoe—
It's mulligan, mulligan, mulligan stew.

Mulligan stew, mulligan stew,
Try it today, you'll be glad when you do.
To unplug a sink or remove a tattoo—
It's mulligan, mulligan, mulligan, mulligan,
    mulligan,
       mulligan
        STEW!

The Dinosaur Dinner

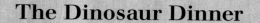

Allosaurus, stegosaurus,
Brontosaurus too,
All went off for dinner at the
Dinosaur zoo.

Along came the waiter, called
Tyrannosaurus Rex,
Gobbled up the table
'Cause they wouldn't pay their checks.

Bundle-buggy Boogie

Well, way up north
On a fine bright day,
A bundle-buggy boogied
At the break of day.

It did the boogie-woogie here,
It did the boogie-woogie there,
It did the bundle-buggy boogie-woogie
Ev-er-y-where:

> *Calabogie,*
> *Kapuskasing,*
> *Espanola,*
> *Atikokan;*
> *Manitoulin,*
> *Madawaska,*
> *Mindemoya,*
> *Moosonee!*

Then another bundle-buggy
Did a boogie-woogie hop,
And another and another
In the bundle-boogie bop.

And it's boogie-woogie high,
And it's boogie-woogie low,
And it's bundle-buggy boogie-woogie
Everywhere you go:

Athabasca,
Abitibi,
Bona Vista,
Malaspina;
Bella Bella,
Bella Coola,
Batchawana,
Baie Comeau!

The Bratty Brother
(Sister)

I dumped the bratty brother
In a shark-infested sea;
By dusk the sea was empty, and
The brat was home with me.

I mailed the bratty brother
To a jail in Moosonee;
The sobbing jailer mailed him
back
The next day, C.O.D.

I wept, and hurled the bratty
Brother off the CN Tower;
He lolloped through the living
room
In less than half an hour.

So now I keep my brother
In the furnace, nice and neat.
I can't wait till December
When my Dad turns on the heat.

Windshield Wipers

Windshield wipers
Wipe away the rain,
Please bring the sunshine
Back again.

Windshield wipers
Clean our car;
The fields are green
And we're travelling far.

My father's coat is warm.
My mother's lap is deep.
Windshield wipers,
Carry me to sleep.

And when I wake,
The sun will be
A golden home
Surrounding me;

But if that rain
Gets worse instead,
I want to sleep
Till I'm in my bed.

Windshield wipers
Wipe away the rain,
Please bring the sunshine
Back again.

Silverly

Silverly,
    Silverly,
Over the
    Trees,
The moon drifts
    By on a
Runaway
    Breeze.

Dozily,
    Dozily,
Deep in her
    Bed,
A little girl
    Dreams with the
Moon in her
    Head.

Dear Reader: Here are some other great Canadian children's books. The ones with a star (★) are suitable for readers aged 4 to 7.

2004 Award-winning Canadian Children's Books

ALBERTA BOOK ILLUSTRATION OF THE YEAR AWARD
★ (Illustration) Marilyn Mets and Peter Ledwon. *In Abby's Hands* by Wendy A. Lewis. Calgary: Red Deer Press, 2003.

ALBERTA CHILDREN'S BOOK OF THE YEAR AWARD
Rudy Wiebe. *Hidden Buffalo*. Paintings by Michael Lonechild. Calgary: Red Deer Press, 2003.

ALCUIN SOCIETY AWARDS FOR EXCELLENCE IN BOOK DESIGN IN CANADA - Children's Category
Lewis Carroll. *Jabberwocky*. Illustrated by Stéphane Jorisch. Toronto: Kids Can Press, 2004.

AMELIA FRANCES HOWARD-GIBBON ILLUSTRATOR'S AWARD
★ (Illustrator) Bill Slavin. *Stanley's Party* by Linda Bailey. Toronto: Kids Can Press, 2003.

ANN CONNOR BRIMER AWARD
Don Aker. *The First Stone*. Toronto: HarperTrophy Canada, 2003.

ARTHUR ELLIS BEST JUVENILE CRIME AWARD
Graham McNamee. *Acceleration*. New York: Random House Children's Books/Wendy Lamb Books, 2003.

BLUE SPRUCE AWARD
★ Linda Bailey. *Stanley's Party*. Illustrated by Bill Slavin. Toronto: Kids Can Press, 2003.

CANADIAN LIBRARY ASSOCIATION BOOK OF THE YEAR FOR CHILDREN AWARD
Brian Doyle. *Boy O' Boy*. Toronto: Groundwood Books, 2003.

CANADIAN LIBRARY ASSOCIATION YOUNG ADULT CANADIAN BOOK AWARD
Polly Horvath. *The Canning Season*. Toronto: Groundwood Books, 2003.

CHOCOLATE LILY YOUNG READERS' CHOICE AWARD
★ (Picture Book) Mary Ann Smith and Katie Smith Milway. *Cappuccina Goes to Town*. Illustrated by Eugenie Fernandes. Toronto: Kids Can Press, 2002.
(Chapter Book/Novel) James Heneghan. *Flood*. Toronto: Groundwood Books, 2002.

CHRISTIE HARRIS ILLUSTRATED CHILDREN'S LITERATURE PRIZE
★ Linda Bailey. *Stanley's Party*. Illustrated by Bill Slavin. Toronto: Kids Can Press, 2003.

DIAMOND WILLOW AWARD
Pat Hancock. *Haunted Canada: True Ghost Stories*. Markham: Scholastic Canada, 2003.

GEOFFREY BILSON AWARD FOR HISTORICAL FICTION FOR YOUNG PEOPLE
Brian Doyle. *Boy O'Boy*. Toronto: Groundwood Books, 2003.

GOLDEN EAGLE CHILDRENS' CHOICE BOOK AWARD
Nicole Luiken. *Violet Eyes*. New York: Pocket Pulse, 2001.

GOLDEN OAK AWARD
Deborah Ellis. *Parvana's Journey*. Toronto: Groundwood Books, 2002.

GOVERNOR GENERAL'S LITERARY AWARDS
(Illustration) Stéphane Jorisch. *Jabberwocky* by Lewis Carroll. Toronto: Kids Can Press, 2004.
(Text) Kenneth Oppel. *Airborn*. Toronto: HarperCollins Canada, 2004.

HACKMATACK CHILDREN'S CHOICE BOOK AWARD
(Fiction) Alan Cumyn. *The Secret Life of Owen Skye*. Toronto: Groundwood Books, 2002.
(Non-Fiction) Karen Levine. *Hana's Suitcase*. Toronto: Second Story Press, 2002.

INFORMATION BOOK AWARD
Shari Graydon. *Made You Look: How Advertising Works and Why You Should Know.* Toronto: Annick Press, 2003.

IODE BOOK AWARD, MUNICIPAL CHAPTER OF TORONTO
★ Kenneth Oppel. *Peg and the Yeti.* Illustrated by Barbara Reid. Toronto: HarperCollins Canada, 2004.

LILLIAN SHEPHERD MEMORIAL AWARD FOR EXCELLENCE IN ILLUSTRATION
(Illustration) Peter Rankin. *Making Room* by Joanne Taylor. Toronto: Tundra Books, 2004.

MANITOBA YOUNG READERS' CHOICE AWARD
Kenneth Oppel. *Firewing.* Toronto: HarperCollins Publishers, 2004.

McNALLY ROBINSON BOOK FOR YOUNG PEOPLE AWARD
(Young Adult) Margaret Bouffie. *The Finder.* Toronto: Kids Can Press, 2004.

NATIONAL CHAPTER OF CANADA IODE VIOLET DOWNEY BOOK AWARD
Sarah Ellis. *The Several Lives of Orphan Jack.* Illustrations by Bruno St-Aubin. Toronto: Groundwood Books, 2003.

NEWFOUNDLAND AND LABRADOR BOOK AWARDS - Bruneau Family Children's/YA Award
Janet McNaughton. *An Earthly Knight.* Toronto: HarperTrophy Canada, 2003

NORMA FLECK AWARD FOR CANADIAN CHILDREN'S NON-FICTION
Val Ross. *The Road to There: Mapmakers and their Stories.* Toronto: Tundra Books, 2003.

RED CEDAR BOOK AWARDS
(Fiction) Virginia Frances Schwartz. *If I Just Had Two Wings.* Toronto: Stoddart Kids, 2001.
(Non-Fiction) Lyn Thomas. *Ha! Ha! Ha! 1000+ Jokes, Riddles, Facts, and More.* Illustrated by Dianne Eastman. Toronto: Maple Tree Press/Owl Books, 2001.

RED MAPLE AWARD
Norah McClintock. *Hit and Run.* Markham, ON: Scholastic Canada, 2003.

ROCKY MOUNTAIN BOOK AWARD
Karen Levine. *Hana's Suitcase.* Toronto: Second Story Press, 2002.

R. ROSS ANNETT AWARD FOR CHILDREN'S LITERATURE
Glen Huser. *Stitches.* Toronto: Groundwood Books, 2003.

RUTH AND SYLVIA SCHWARTZ CHILDREN'S BOOK AWARD
★(Picture Book) Barbara Reid. *The Subway Mouse.* Markham, ON: North Winds Press/Scholastic Canada, 2003.
(YA-Middle Reader) Brian Doyle. *Boy O' Boy.* Toronto: Groundwood Books, 2003.

SASKATCHEWAN BOOK AWARDS
(Children's) Beth Goobie. *Flux.* Victoria: Orca Book Publishers, 2004.

SHEILA A. EGOFF CHILDREN'S LITERATURE PRIZE
Dennis Foon. *Skud.* Toronto: Groundwood Books, 2003.

SHINING WILLOW AWARD
★Linda Bailey. *Stanley's Party.* Illustrated by Bill Slavin. Toronto: Kids Can Press, 2003.

SILVER BIRCH AWARD
(Fiction) Michael McGowan. *Newton and the Giant.* Toronto: HarperCollins Canada, 2003.
(Non-Fiction) Larry Verstraete. *Survivors! True Death-Defying Escapes.* Markham, ON: Scholastic Canada, 2003.

SNOW WILLOW AWARD
Barbara Haworth-Attard. *Theories of Relativity.* Toronto: Harper-Trophy Canada, 2003.

TINY TORGI LITERARY AWARDS
★(PrintBraille) Linda Bailey. *Stanley's Party.* Illustrated by Bill Slavin. Toronto: Kids Can Press, 2003.
(Audio) Eric Walters. *Run.* Toronto: Penguin Canada, 2003.

WHITE PINE AWARD
Don Aker. *The First Stone.* Toronto: HarperTrophy Canada, 2003.

TD Canadian Children's Book Week

Approximately 500,000 Grade One children across Canada will receive a copy of this book, *Alligator Stew*. This special book giveaway is part of the celebration of TD Canadian Children's Book Week, which takes place from October 29 to November 5, 2005.

TD Canadian Children's Book Week is the largest annual celebration of Canadian books and reading in schools and libraries. During Book Week, Canadian authors, illustrators, and storytellers tour across the country visiting schools, libraries and community centres to talk about their books and meet young readers.

Book Week also inspires many independent activities and local celebrations of Canadian children's books and their creators.

The Grade One Book Giveaway and TD Canadian Children's Book Week are organized by the Canadian Children's Book Centre. The Canadian Children's Book Centre is a national, not-for-profit organization founded in 1976, dedicated to promoting the reading, writing, and illustrating of Canadian books for young readers.

TD Canadian Children's Book Week is made possible through the generous support of the following sponsors and funders:

Title Sponsor: TD Bank Financial Group
Major Sponsor: Canada Council for the Arts
Associate Sponsors: Amazon.ca; Imperial Oil Foundation; Library and Archives
                          Canada; Ontario Arts Council; Penguin Group (Canada);
                          Toronto Public Library

For more information on the Canadian Children's Book Centre and TD Canadian Children's Book Week, please visit our websites at **www.bookcentre.ca** and **www.bookweek.ca**. You can also call us, or write to us at:

The Canadian Children's Book Centre
Suite 101, 40 Orchard View Blvd.
Toronto, Ontario
M4R 1B9

Telephone: (416) 975-0010
Fax: (416) 975-8970
Email: info@bookcentre.ca
Websites: www.bookcentre.ca
             www.bookweek.ca

The Canadian Children's Book Centre

Bringing Canadian books and young readers together.